D1363430

Handwriting is part of Primary English whether they like it or not

'Handwriting Heaven or Handwriting Hell' works by setting clear targets. We think kids do better if they know exactly what they're being asked to do...

> **BY THE END OF THE YEAR YOU HAVE TO WRITE USING CONSISTENT AND APPROPRIATE JOINING LINES THAT JOIN <u>CONSISTENTLY</u> SIZED LETTERS.**

...and this book gives kids lots of <u>practice</u> to <u>make sure they do</u>.

Here's how it works...

1) Make sure the whole class knows that:
   - the point of this book is to GET INTO HANDWRITING HEAVEN
   - you stay in Heaven by <u>meeting targets</u>
   - to do well in primary English you must <u>write everything in a joined up style</u>.

2) We've left a space for you to write a target at the top of each page, eg. 5/20.

3) Targets should get <u>tougher</u> over the year.

4) If a child meets their target, they're in Handwriting Heaven, but if they miss one they go to Handwriting Hell — until next time they meet their targets.

5) Then you can circle the Heaven or Hell at the top of each page.

6) Even better, make a massive poster, with stickers for the kids' names. Move the names from Hell to Heaven in a weekly ceremony. Give prizes for going to Heaven, and punishments for going to Hell — may we suggest running round the school waving their hands in the air shouting, "I hate turnips! I hate turnips!" *

* Because, as everyone knows, in Handwriting Hell they make you eat turnips, while sitting in a bath full of rotten baked beans.

Joining to the letter 'i'

1) William likes digging in the dirt.

2) It is slimy and disgusting.

3) It makes him very ill.

4) The other kids think he's weird.

5) He thinks they are a bit boring.

6) Sheila likes bikes.

7) Claire hates heights.

8) Alice is in massive trouble.

9) She climbed on top of a pig.

10) The pig didn't like it much.

11) Bill sits down for his dinner.

12) He eats five tins of mince.

13) He eats eight pink biscuits.

14) He drinks a litre of liquid lard.

15) Bill is sick nine times.

16) I want a shiny bike for my birthday.

17) I have mice in my kitchen.

18) I hate tidying things.

19) There is a dinosaur in the city.

20) I wish I had a dish of chips.

Joining to the letter "i"

ai ....   ci ....   mi ....

ni ....   di ....   hi ....   li ....

1) ....

2) ....

3) ....

4) ....

5) ....

6) ....

7) ....

8) ....

9) ....

10) ....

11) ....

12) ....

13) ....

14) ....

15) ....

16) ....

17) ....

18) ....

19) ....

20) ....

Joining to the letter 'o'

1) I love going to school.

2) I adore homework.

3) I'm not joking, honestly.

4) Shona phoned up Thomas.

5) Some people don't like dogs.

6) Simon won't go to town.

7) The song is a bit too long.

8) Simone's pet is a yellow mole.

9) It runs around the floor.

10) Do you know any frogs?

11) My brother is a slob.

12) He is also a doctor.

13) Through the door is another room.

14) The toilet is downstairs.

15) There is a balcony at the front.

16) I won't go to the doctor.

17) My favourite colour is orange.

18) The boy fell down on the ground.

19) Tom's hobby is growing plants.

20) His tomato plants are monstrous.

Joining to the letter 'o'

co ....   mo ....   no ....

do ....   ho ....   lo ....

1)
2)
3)
4)
5)
6)
7)
8)
9)
10)
11)
12)
13)
14)
15)
16)
17)
18)
19)
20)

Joining to the letter 'a'

In order to reach Handwriting Heaven, make sure that in ☐ out of 20 of the sentences below, the letter 'a' is written and joined correctly.

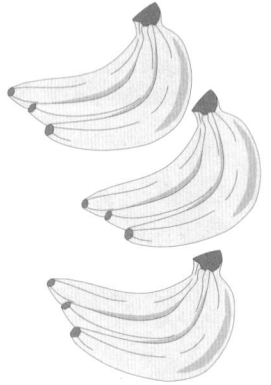

1) Amanda draws trains.

2) Sarah watches planes.

3) Beavis eats bananas.

4) Maria was eaten by an alligator.

5) The alligator was happy.

6) I like dancing in the park.

7) The leaves look beautiful.

8) Parrots are dreadful animals.

9) Sharon was given a huge coat.

10) I haven't got any mandarins.

11) My gran lives out on the lawn.

12) She says it's great.

13) She has a tent and lots to eat.

14) She has many layers of blankets.

15) She says that she is happy.

16) Be careful in the cellar.

17) It's dark and dangerous.

18) Small animals live under the stairs.

19) They can kill humans easily.

20) You should always wear a mask.

Joining to the letter 'a'

ca ....   ea ....   ma ....

na ....   da ....   ha ....   la ....

1) ....

2) ....

3) ....

4) ....

5) ....

6) ....

7) ....

8) ....

9) ....

10) ....

11) ....

12) ....

13) ....

14) ....

15) ....

16) ....

17) ....

18) ....

19) ....

20) ....

Joining to the letter 'e'

In order to reach Handwriting Heaven, make sure that in ☐ out of 20 of the sentences below, the letter 'e' is written and joined correctly.

1) The men wanted a big meal.

2) They ordered curry and rice.

3) They were given lettuce.

4) They asked to see the owner.

5) The meal ended badly.

6) Joseph hates me.

7) I'm not sure what I've done.

8) Maybe it's because I ate his tea.

9) I went to his house on Wednesday.

10) His mum didn't realise it was me.

11) I went to the village market.

12) Women were selling hens.

13) The price was too high for me.

14) I bought some eggs instead.

15) Fried eggs are nice.

16) Jane met them at the stile.

17) She loved the purple wallpaper.

18) The vicar told a horrible tale.

19) The medicine worked well.

20) He never burped again.

Joining to the letter 'e'

ce ....   me ....   ne ....

de ....   he ....   le ....

1) ....

2) ....

3) ....

4) ....

5) ....

6) ....

7) ....

8) ....

9) ....

10) ....

11) ....

12) ....

13) ....

14) ....

15) ....

16) ....

17) ....

18) ....

19) ....

20) ....

Joining to the letter 'r'

In order to reach Handwriting Heaven, make sure that in ☐ out of 20 of the sentences below, the letter 'r' is written and joined correctly.

1) It's my party.

2) I'll cry if I want to.

3) Give me a drink of pure water.

4) There is a growth on my finger.

5) Germany is a big country.

6) Mary learnt how to draw today.

7) Her picture was terrible.

8) She will never be an artist.

9) Sarah's horse has three heads.

10) Gary's hamster has four noses.

11) I dare you to write on the wall.

12) I'm scared of spiders.

13) My arm was in danger of breaking.

14) Sandra drove round the sharp bend.

15) Gary's hamster smells dreadful.

16) The strange teacher screamed.

17) Mary sang in the choir today.

18) Her singing was crazy.

19) She will never be an opera singer.

20) The teacher argued with my gran.

Joining to the letter 'r'

ar ....   cr ....   er ....

ir ....   ur ....   dr ....

1) ....

2) ....

3) ....

4) ....

5) ....

6) ....

7) ....

8) ....

9) ....

10) ....

11) ....

12) ....

13) ....

14) ....

15) ....

16) ....

17) ....

18) ....

19) ....

20) ....

Joining to the letters 'm' and 'n'

In order to reach Handwriting Heaven, make sure that in ☐ out of 20 of the sentences below, the letters 'm' and 'n' are written and joined correctly.

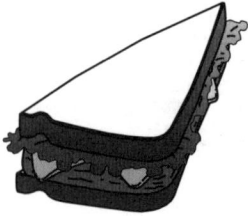

1) Jenny wants a cream bun.

2) I want a ham sandwich.

3) John doesn't want anything.

4) I have giant fingers.

5) My mum is angry and annoyed.

6) Tony's tummy hurts.

7) He feels very glum.

8) Running the country is hard.

9) Jane ran away from the ants.

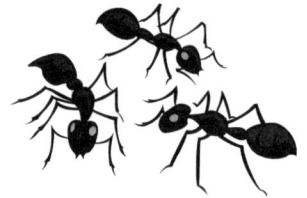

10) She can't stand them.

11) The honey was runny.

12) Money is a funny thing.

13) "I am what I am," sang Tracy.

14) Then we can go to the moon.

15) It's sunny at this time of year.

16) There are pennies in the fountain.

17) Gordon found spam in the jam.

18) Tom runs around all the time.

19) Honey, I shrank the kids.

20) My dad is under my mum's thumb.

Joining to the letters 'm' and 'n'

am ....   em ....   um ....

an ....   en ....   un ....

1) ....

2) ....

3) ....

4) ....

5) ....

6) ....

7) ....

8) ....

9) ....

10) ....

11) ....

12) ....

13) ....

14) ....

15) ....

16) ....

17) ....

18) ....

19) ....

20) ....

Joining to the letters 'u', 'w' and 'y'

In order to reach Handwriting Heaven, make sure that in ☐ out of 20 of the sentences below, the letters 'u', 'w' and 'y' are written and joined correctly.

1) You are a very naughty boy.

2) I was sawn in half.

3) We built a den in the sand dunes.

4) There are hundreds of ducks.

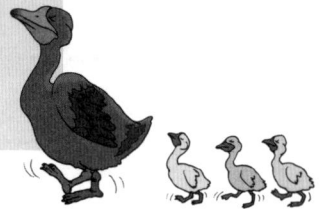

5) The ewe was hungry.

6) The mashed potato was lumpy.

7) The eggs were raw.

8) The sheep eyes were huge.

9) Paul ate them and felt awful.

10) The lunch went on forever.

11) The key is in the drawer.

12) Saul drew a beautiful gerbil.

13) I've had too much education.

14) They had an audition for the play.

15) A few people saw you leave.

16) The Duke dunked the biscuit.

17) Paul saw everything.

18) The lawyer eyed the money.

19) The plan was flawed.

20) I crawled to the house.

Joining to the letters 'u', 'w' and 'y'

au ....   eu ....   du ....   ey ....

hu ....   lu ....   aw ....   ew ....

1) ....

2) ....

3) ....

4) ....

5) ....

6) ....

7) ....

8) ....

9) ....

10) ....

11) ....

12) ....

13) ....

14) ....

15) ....

16) ....

17) ....

18) ....

19) ....

20) ....

Joining to the letters 'p', 'g' and 'c'

In order to reach Handwriting Heaven, make sure that in ☐ out of 20 of the sentences below, the letters 'p', 'g' and 'c' are written and joined correctly.

1) The jug blew up.

2) It broke into five pieces.

3) I swept it up.

4) I wiped away my tears.

5) It was a nice jug.

6) Macy has got lots of mugs.

7) My gran sips tea out of a cup.

8) I approached the gate quietly.

9) We use apparatus in science.

10) Mind the gaps.

11) According to Maggie, I have lice.

12) I was up in the clouds.

13) I was dreaming of happy magpies.

14) I came eighth in the sack race.

15) I ate too much pepper at supper.

16) I dug up some acorns.

17) The apples are ripe.

18) I jumped up to the attic.

19) The mice are huge.

20) I left quickly.

Joining to the letters 'p', 'g' and 'c'

ap ....   ep ....   ip ....

up ....   ug ....   ic ....   ac ....

1) ....

2) ....

3) ....

4) ....

5) ....

6) ....

7) ....

8) ....

9) ....

10) ....

11) ....

12) ....

13) ....

14) ....

15) ....

16) ....

17) ....

18) ....

19) ....

20) ....

Joining from the letter 'o'

In order to reach Handwriting Heaven, make sure that in [ ] out of 20 of the sentences below, the letter 'o' is written and joined correctly.

1) Tom moans about the noise.

2) Joan loves poached eggs.

3) Dominic has a new moped.

4) Horses love oats.

5) Popcorn and movies are good.

6) My socks are old.

7) Don't mop up the oil.

8) The ogre ate my friend.

9) I shouted for it to stop.

10) Now my voice is hoarse.

11) There's a frog in my pocket.

12) I hope I will have enough soap.

13) The chips are soggy and brown.

14) The operation was very gory.

15) We're going to move to Preston.

16) The bus was lost in the bog.

17) The loaf was mouldy.

18) I locked the fox in the bathroom.

19) I didn't know any of the people.

20) I was given shop vouchers.

Joining from the letter 'o'

oa ....   oc ....   og ....   ov ....

oi ....   op ....   om ....   on ....

1) ....

2) ....

3) ....

4) ....

5) ....

6) ....

7) ....

8) ....

9) ....

10) ....

11) ....

12) ....

13) ....

14) ....

15) ....

16) ....

17) ....

18) ....

19) ....

20) ....

Joining from the letter 'w'

In order to reach Handwriting Heaven, make sure that in ☐ out of 20 of the sentences below, the letter 'w' is written and joined correctly.

1) I went to the water's edge.

2) There was a wooden bridge.

3) I walked across with my wife.

4) She is a heavy woman.

5) The bridge was weak.

6) She swam for shore.

7) A walrus bit her with its jaws.

8) I swung from a branch.

9) I hit it with my walking stick.

10) I saved my wimpy wife.

11) I was wonderful.

12) She was soaking wet.

13) She wanted a woolly blanket.

14) I wasn't interested in getting warm.

15) I wanted to throw a party.

16) I bought some sweets.

17) I washed my walking stick.

18) I wore a new waistcoat.

19) I met twelve friends in town.

20) I ordered wine from the waiter.

Joining from the letter 'w'

wa ....   we ....   wi ....

wo ....   wu ....   ws ....

1) ....
2) ....
3) ....
4) ....
5) ....
6) ....
7) ....
8) ....
9) ....
10) ....
11) ....
12) ....
13) ....
14) ....
15) ....
16) ....
17) ....
18) ....
19) ....
20) ....

Joining from the letter 'v'

1) The man vanished.

2) The vulture dived on the doves.

3) The doves fell over.

4) They were very nervous.

5) I bravely saved them all.

6) Oliver hid in the cave.

7) The vicar lost his voice.

8) He could never leave.

9) Give me some ravioli.

10) The vinegar was vile.

11) The foxgloves are in the vase.

12) The view from the verge is great.

13) Olivia must sieve the flour.

14) She lives in Scandinavia.

15) People eat vine leaves in Greece.

16) Sylvia searched in vain.

17) He votes for the Conservatives.

18) Lava came out of the volcano.

19) The vole was vicious.

20) The video was overly violent.

Joining from the letter 'v'

va ....   ve ....   vi ....

vo ....   vu ....

1) ....

2) ....

3) ....

4) ....

5) ....

6) ....

7) ....

8) ....

9) ....

10) ....

11) ....

12) ....

13) ....

14) ....

15) ....

16) ....

17) ....

18) ....

19) ....

20) ....

Joining from the letter 't'

In order to reach Handwriting Heaven, make sure that in ☐ out of 20 of the sentences below, the letter 't' is written and joined correctly.

1) The elephant's trunk was twisted.

2) The truck stopped at the station.

3) I trained the cats to do tricks.

4) Now they can talk and tap dance.

5) I tell them to stop talking.

6) The tune was terribly catchy.

7) I have a tattoo on my tummy.

8) Peter waited outside for a minute.

9) The inspector was at the entrance.

10) The taxi stopped in a tunnel.

11) I tasted the toothpaste.

12) I took twenty photos of my teeth.

13) I ate two slices of toast.

14) My mate Kate hates tea.

15) I think it's fantastic.

16) My twin is called Henrietta.

17) She's better than me at maths.

18) My teacher is called Loretta.

19) She talks about train times a lot.

20) I took my tutu out of the trunk.

Joining from the letter 't'

ta .... te .... ti ....

to .... tr .... tu .... tw ....

1) ....

2) ....

3) ....

4) ....

5) ....

6) ....

7) ....

8) ....

9) ....

10) ....

11) ....

12) ....

13) ....

14) ....

15) ....

16) ....

17) ....

18) ....

19) ....

20) ....

Joining from the letter 'f'

In order to reach Handwriting Heaven, make sure that in ☐ out of 20 of the sentences below, the letter 'f' is written and joined correctly.

1) My feet are frozen.

2) I fell off a fir tree into a foxhole.

3) I'm feeling feeble and faint.

4) Make me a fire and find me food.

5) Fish and fries would be nice.

6) My friend is a famous footballer.

7) My father is a firefighter.

8) My wife makes finger puppets.

9) Life is full of freaky events.

10) Frodo is a funny name.

11) In France they eat figs and frogs.

12) He found four fish in a field.

13) Does eating fries make you fat?

14) Alfred forgot all his food.

15) He foraged in the forest for nuts.

16) My friend is afraid of horror films.

17) That shark's fin is frightening.

18) The future is too far away.

19) I just want to have fun.

20) I froze in fear of the frog.

Joining from the letter 'f'

fa ....   fe ....   fi ....

fo ....   fu ....   fr ....

1) ....

2) ....

3) ....

4) ....

5) ....

6) ....

7) ....

8) ....

9) ....

10) ....

11) ....

12) ....

13) ....

14) ....

15) ....

16) ....

17) ....

18) ....

19) ....

20) ....

Joining to the letter 'l'

In order to reach Handwriting Heaven, make sure that in ⬚ out of 20 of the sentences below, the letter 'l' is written and joined correctly.

1) Sally's clothes are clean.

2) The sloth was slow.

3) Eels are not clever.

4) Phil pulled open the door.

5) The bull ran into the palace.

6) I can sell anything.

7) Pass the salt.

8) Rachel's arm was in a sling.

9) She fell into a pile of slugs.

10) Paul won't allow that.

11) Gillian stole several seagulls.

12) Tell me about the woodlouse.

13) The seal had a huge meal.

14) She says television is dull.

15) Football is close to my heart.

16) Bill walked into the wall.

17) He pulled out a plane ticket.

18) He yelled, "I want to go to Nepal."

19) Chocolate is brilliant.

20) I really like gerbils.

Joining to the letter 'l'

al ....   cl ....   el ....

il ....   ul ....   sl ....

1)

2)

3)

4)

5)

6)

7)

8)

9)

10)

11)

12)

13)

14)

15)

16)

17)

18)

19)

20)

Joining to the letter 't'

In order to reach Handwriting Heaven, make sure that in [ ] out of 20 of the sentences below, the letter 't' is written and joined correctly.

1) My Aunt Kit is trying to get fit.

2) Rita is stuck in a rut.

3) It's a pity the city is so dirty.

4) I bet the rat wins the race.

5) He went without his coat.

6) Justin has a big stain on his hat.

7) I haven't got the guts to tell him.

8) Peter attacked his mate Pat.

9) She had stolen his pet bat.

10) Football is the best sport ever.

11) Let me come and play in your flat.

12) I can fit eight cats in my hat.

13) The fat cat sat on the mat.

14) He would not give out information.

15) The mattress was scratchy.

16) Just write a letter.

17) Put some water in the trap.

18) You'll catch thirsty rats.

19) What more could you want?

20) Do not forget to eat the nuts.

Joining to the letter 't'

at ....   et ....   it ....

st ....   ut ....

1)
2)
3)
4)
5)
6)
7)
8)
9)
10)
11)
12)
13)
14)
15)
16)
17)
18)
19)
20)

Joining to the letter 'b'

In order to reach Handwriting Heaven, make sure that in ☐ out of 20 of the sentences below, the letter 'b' is written and joined correctly.

1) Robin has a tabby cat.

2) I hate rhubarb crumble.

3) I got lost in the subway.

4) Elizabeth stole my rubber ball.

5) The jumble sale was smelly.

6) Gaby lost the baby's bib.

7) She dropped it in some rubble.

8) Amber wears grubby socks.

9) I ambled to the library.

10) I wanted to find out about rabies.

11) Rub some salt on it.

12) My rabbit always obeys me.

13) Are you able to do that?

14) My brother has lots of debt.

15) I hate homework club.

16) I broke my rib in February.

17) It still hadn't healed in September.

18) Remember the 5th of November.

19) Sebastian carried some timber.

20) I clambered aboard ship.

Joining to the letter 'b'

ab ....   eb ....   mb ....

ub ....   ib ....

1) ....

2) ....

3) ....

4) ....

5) ....

6) ....

7) ....

8) ....

9) ....

10) ....

11) ....

12) ....

13) ....

14) ....

15) ....

16) ....

17) ....

18) ....

19) ....

20) ....

Joining to the letter 'f'

In order to reach Handwriting Heaven, make sure that in ☐ out of 20 of the sentences below, the letter 'f' is written and joined correctly.

1) The lift is on the left.

2) The beef was old and stiff.

3) I gave it to Jeff as a gift.

4) He sniffed it and jumped off a cliff.

5) Luckily, he landed on a raft.

6) I wanted to avoid the riff-raff.

7) I went to a cafe with Steffi Graf.

8) We had a ride on a giraffe.

9) It was not very safe.

10) It was a relief to go back to the raft.

11) My teacher is stuffy and gruff.

12) He is always in a huff.

13) He made me draw a leaf.

14) It looked like a duffle coat.

15) I can't draw for toffee.

16) He sifted through the old photos.

17) I ran after the head of staff.

18) Hanif snuffed out the light.

19) The sound was muffled.

20) I looked a gift horse in the mouth.

Joining to the letter 'f'

af ....   ef ....

if ....   uf ....

1) ....

2) ....

3) ....

4) ....

5) ....

6) ....

7) ....

8) ....

9) ....

10) ....

11) ....

12) ....

13) ....

14) ....

15) ....

16) ....

17) ....

18) ....

19) ....

20) ....

Joining to the letters 'h' and 'k'

In order to reach Handwriting Heaven, make sure that in ☐ out of 20 of the sentences below, the letters 'h' and 'k' are written and joined correctly.

1) The chicken was quick to run.

2) The bike skidded to a halt.

3) Lock up your cheese.

4) Pink is the worst colour.

5) Saskia has ink in her mouth.

6) Frank is rubbish at hockey.

7) Kicking the ball is cheating.

8) Michael is a punk with pink hair.

9) My teacher loves mashed potato.

10) Josh found sheep on the beach.

11) The big match is in March.

12) The brakes on my bike broke.

13) Rick shaved off his beard.

14) I took a cheque to the bank.

15) The mask hid a double chin.

16) Go on a trek in the shrubbery.

17) You should see a skunk.

18) Jack thanked the teacher.

19) She'd found his socks and shirt.

20) He plonked the letter on the desk.

Joining to the letters 'h' and 'k'

ch ....   ck ....   sh ....

ek ....   sk ....   nk ....

1) ....

2) ....

3) ....

4) ....

5) ....

6) ....

7) ....

8) ....

9) ....

10) ....

11) ....

12) ....

13) ....

14) ....

15) ....

16) ....

17) ....

18) ....

19) ....

20) ....

Joining from the letter 'o'

In order to reach Handwriting Heaven, make sure that in ☐ out of 20 of the sentences below, the letter 'o' is written and joined correctly.

1) Noddy is an odd man.

2) He has a lot of spooky stories.

3) He robs footballs from shops.

4) He hates goldfish and otters.

5) He told my mum he was a crook.

6) I sold four books and an old boot.

7) The ground shook.

8) I hid in the loft with my brother.

9) Cod-liver oil is revolting.

10) My body turned into a blob.

11) I ran amok in the town centre.

12) You can stroke the parrot.

13) Roland was a rotten cook.

14) Polly had a pot of gold.

15) Molly had a log of wood.

16) I cooked hot noodles in my wok.

17) I lobbed the ball to Geoffrey.

18) I forgot my name when I woke up.

19) My brother said it was Gollum.

20) But really it was Bob.

Joining from the letter 'o'

ob ....   od ....   of ....

ok ....   ol ....   ot ....

1) ....

2) ....

3) ....

4) ....

5) ....

6) ....

7) ....

8) ....

9) ....

10) ....

11) ....

12) ....

13) ....

14) ....

15) ....

16) ....

17) ....

18) ....

19) ....

20) ....

Joining from the letter 'w'

In order to reach Handwriting Heaven, make sure that in ☐ out of 20 of the sentences below, the letter 'w' is written and joined correctly.

1) Moby Dick was a whale.

2) The newt was evil.

3) My dad's car only has one wheel.

4) Do you know where Northwich is?

5) The whirlpool was scary.

6) Our dog howls at the moon.

7) He growls at clocks.

8) He chases owls.

9) He chews my gran's shawl.

10) He ate the white rabbit.

11) Do you know what the film's about?

12) The whole thing is just silly.

13) My uncle loves whisky.

14) The baby kept bawling.

15) Do you know who she is?

16) He whipped his horse.

17) He prowled around the house.

18) She scowled at the hamster.

19) It ran round on its wheel.

20) She took away the food bowl.

Joining from the letter 'w'

wh .... wl .... wt ....

1) ....

2) ....

3) ....

4) ....

5) ....

6) ....

7) ....

8) ....

9) ....

10) ....

11) ....

12) ....

13) ....

14) ....

15) ....

16) ....

17) ....

18) ....

19) ....

20) ....

Practice of all join types

In order to reach Handwriting Heaven, make sure that in ☐ out of 20 of the sentences below, all the letters are written and joined correctly.

1) Janet falls into the hedge.

2) She has leaves in her hair.

3) There is soil on her shoe.

4) She says, "Who pushed me?"

5) I am hiding in the girl's toilets.

6) Petula hit the elephant.

7) It sat on her husband.

8) She grabbed its trunk and pulled.

9) It rampaged over the rose bed.

10) It was a fight to the death.

11) Charles waited for the bus.

12) Ten years later he was still there.

13) I want the top bunk.

14) Paul stuck his tongue out.

15) His mum rolled her eyes.

16) The flamingo ate me for lunch.

17) Michelle likes chip sandwiches.

18) Josh scored six goals in a row.

19) I like singing badly.

20) Harvey was a skating champion.

Practice of all join types

1)

2)

3)

4)

5)

6)

7)

8)

9)

10)

11)

12)

13)

14)

15)

16)

17)

18)

19)

20)

Practice of all join types

In order to reach Handwriting Heaven, make sure that in [ ] out of 20 of the sentences below, all the letters are written and joined correctly.

1) Gary is a belly dancer.

2) Jane is a plumber at the palace.

3) The Queen gave her a giraffe.

4) Now she can ride to work in style.

5) Simone is a snake charmer.

6) A Viking lives in my shed.

7) There's a Roman in my bed.

8) A caveman sleeps in the lounge.

9) His pet dinosaur is called Fred.

10) My family moved out.

11) My mum loves Robert Mitchum.

12) Callum sat in the mud.

13) My hamster smiles all the time.

14) I don't know what's so funny.

15) Why is grass green?

16) Slugs are really cute.

17) I fell over and scraped my knee.

18) What would I do without TV?

19) My teacher said, "Quiet please".

20) My tummy gurgled very loudly.